Personal Health Record Keeper

ATIELA
PUBLICATIONS

VANCOUVER, WA

Published by Atiela Publications in 2020.
© Design and writing: 2020 Atiela Journals. All rights reserved.

Front cover images from:
Blood Sugar Meter by HelgaMariah/Shutterstock.com
Doctor's clipboard by Abscent/Shutterstock.com
Blood Pressure Monitor by Double Brain/Shutterstock.com
Pill Bottle by Panimoni/Shutterstock.com

Visit atielajournals.com for more log books, journals, and planners.
ISBN: 978-1-947965-11-9

Contents

My Information

Name: _____

Address: _____

_____

Home Phone: _____

Cell Phone: _____

Email: _____

Date of Birth: _____

Emergency Contacts

Name: _____

Home Phone: _____

Cell Phone: _____

Relationship: _____

Name: _____

Home Phone: _____

Cell Phone: _____

Relationship: _____

Name: _____

Home Phone: _____

Cell Phone: _____

Relationship: _____

Medical Profile

Date of Birth: _____   **Blood Type:** _____

Allergies

1. _____   6. _____

2. _____   7. _____

3. _____   8. _____

4. _____   9. _____

5. _____   10. _____

Major Illnesses

1. _____   6. _____

2. _____   7. _____

3. _____   8. _____

4. _____   9. _____

5. _____   10. _____

Surgeries

Date: _____   Surgery: _____

Date: _____   Surgery: _____

Date: _____   Surgery: _____

Date: _____   Surgery: _____

Date: _____   Surgery: _____

Medicines / Vitamins

Name	Dose	How Often	What It's For

Medicines / Vitamins

Name	Dose	How Often	What It's For

Medicines / Vitamins

Name	Dose	How Often	What It's For

Medicines / Vitamins

Name	Dose	How Often	What It's For

Medicines / Vitamins

Name	Dose	How Often	What It's For

Doctors

Type of Dr:	
Name:	
Practice:	
Address:	
Phone:	
Website:	
Login:	*Password:*
Notes:	

Type of Dr:	
Name:	
Practice:	
Address:	
Phone:	
Website:	
Login:	*Password:*
Notes:	

Doctors

Type of Dr:	
Name:	
Practice:	
Address:	
Phone:	
Website:	
Login:	*Password:*
Notes:	

Type of Dr:	
Name:	
Practice:	
Address:	
Phone:	
Website:	
Login:	*Password:*
Notes:	

Doctors

Type of Dr:	
Name:	
Practice:	
Address:	
Phone:	
Website:	
Login:	Password:
Notes:	

Type of Dr:	
Name:	
Practice:	
Address:	
Phone:	
Website:	
Login:	Password:
Notes:	

Doctors

Type of Dr:	
Name:	
Practice:	
Address:	
Phone:	
Website:	
Login:	*Password:*
Notes:	

Type of Dr:	
Name:	
Practice:	
Address:	
Phone:	
Website:	
Login:	*Password:*
Notes:	

Pharmacies

Name:	
Address:	
Phone:	
Website:	
Login:	Password:
Notes:	

Name:	
Address:	
Phone:	
Website:	
Login:	Password:
Notes:	

Name:	
Address:	
Phone:	
Website:	
Login:	Password:
Notes:	

Pharmacies

Name:	
Address:	
Phone:	
Website:	
Login:	Password:
Notes:	

Name:	
Address:	
Phone:	
Website:	
Login:	Password:
Notes:	

Name:	
Address:	
Phone:	
Website:	
Login:	Password:
Notes:	

Medical Insurance

Provider:	
Phone:	
Website:	

Login:		*Password:*	
Contract #:		*Group #:*	
Start Date:		*Deductible:*	

Provider:	
Phone:	
Website:	

Login:		*Password:*	
Contract #:		*Group #:*	
Start Date:		*Deductible:*	

Provider:	
Phone:	
Website:	

Login:		*Password:*	
Contract #:		*Group #:*	
Start Date:		*Deductible:*	

Medical Insurance

Provider:	
Phone:	
Website:	
Login:	*Password:*
Contract #:	*Group #:*
Start Date:	*Deductible:*

Provider:	
Phone:	
Website:	
Login:	*Password:*
Contract #:	*Group #:*
Start Date:	*Deductible:*

Provider:	
Phone:	
Website:	
Login:	*Password:*
Contract #:	*Group #:*
Start Date:	*Deductible:*

Medical Expenses

Date	Expense	Cost
		Total

Medical Expenses

Date	Expense	Cost
	Total	

Medical Expenses

Date	Expense	Cost
	Total	

Doctor Visits

Date:		*Time:*	
Doctor:			
Reason for Visit:			
Questions to Ask:			
Notes:			
Next Visit:			

Date:		*Time:*	
Doctor:			
Reason for Visit:			
Questions to Ask:			
Notes:			
Next Visit:			

Doctor Visits

Date:		Time:	
Doctor:			
Reason for Visit:			
Questions to Ask:			
Notes:			
Next Visit:			

Date:		Time:	
Doctor:			
Reason for Visit:			
Questions to Ask:			
Notes:			
Next Visit:			

Doctor Visits

Date:		Time:	
Doctor:			
Reason for Visit:			
Questions to Ask:			
Notes:			
Next Visit:			

Date:		Time:	
Doctor:			
Reason for Visit:			
Questions to Ask:			
Notes:			
Next Visit:			

Doctor Visits

Date:		**Time:**	
Doctor:			
Reason for Visit:			
Questions to Ask:			
Notes:			
Next Visit:			

Date:		**Time:**	
Doctor:			
Reason for Visit:			
Questions to Ask:			
Notes:			
Next Visit:			

Doctor Visits

Date:		*Time:*	
Doctor:			
Reason for Visit:			
Questions to Ask:			
Notes:			
Next Visit:			

Date:		*Time:*	
Doctor:			
Reason for Visit:			
Questions to Ask:			
Notes:			
Next Visit:			

Doctor Visits

Date:		**Time:**	
Doctor:			
Reason for Visit:			
Questions to Ask:			
Notes:			
Next Visit:			

Date:		**Time:**	
Doctor:			
Reason for Visit:			
Questions to Ask:			
Notes:			
Next Visit:			

Blood Pressure Chart

My Target Blood Pressure: _____ / _____

Blood Pressure Category	SYSTOLIC mm Hg (Upper Number)		DIASTOLIC mm Hg (Lower Number)
NORMAL	LESS THAN 120	and	LESS THAN 80
ELEVATED	120 - 129	and	LESS THAN 80
HIGH BLOOD PRESSURE (Hypertension) Stage 1	130 - 139	or	80 - 89
HIGH BLOOD PRESSURE (Hypertension) Stage 2	140 or HIGHER	or	90 OR HIGHER
HYPERTENSIVE CRISIS (Consult your doctor immediately)	HIGHER THAN 180	and/or	HIGHER THAN 120

Source: American Heart Association

Be sure to consult your doctor if you have questions about the chart or your own blood pressure readings.

Blood Sugar Targets

My Target Fasting Blood Sugar: _____ mg/dL

My Target Blood Sugar After a Meal: _____ mg/dL

The American Diabetes Association suggests the following blood sugar targets for most nonpregnant adults with diabetes:

When	Blood Sugar Target
Before a meal (preprandial plasma glucose)	80-130 mg/dL
1-2 hours after beginning of the meal (postprandial plasma glucose)	Less than 180 mg/dL

Low blood sugar (also known as hypoglycemia) is usually when your blood sugar is less than 70 mg/dL.

Please consult your diabetes care team on how to recognize and treat high and low blood sugar levels.

Source: American Diabetes Association

Be sure to consult your doctor for your target blood sugar levels.

Weekly Notes

Monday: _____
_____
_____
_____

Tuesday: _____
_____
_____
_____

Wednesday: _____
_____
_____
_____

Thursday: _____
_____
_____
_____

Friday: _____
_____
_____
_____

Saturday: _____
_____
_____
_____

Sunday: _____
_____
_____
_____

Weekly Tracking

Date / Weight	Time	Blood Sugar	Blood Press.	Pulse
Monday				
Weight				
Tuesday				
Weight				
Wednesday				
Weight				
Thursday				
Weight				
Friday				
Weight				
Saturday				
Weight				
Sunday				
Weight				

Weekly Notes

Monday: _____
_____
_____
_____

Tuesday: _____
_____
_____
_____

Wednesday: _____
_____
_____
_____

Thursday: _____
_____
_____
_____

Friday: _____
_____
_____
_____

Saturday: _____
_____
_____
_____

Sunday: _____
_____
_____
_____

Weekly Tracking

Date / Weight	Time	Blood Sugar	Blood Press.	Pulse
Monday				
Weight				
Tuesday				
Weight				
Wednesday				
Weight				
Thursday				
Weight				
Friday				
Weight				
Saturday				
Weight				
Sunday				
Weight				

Weekly Notes

Monday: _____
_____
_____
_____

Tuesday: _____
_____
_____
_____

Wednesday: _____
_____
_____
_____

Thursday: _____
_____
_____
_____

Friday: _____
_____
_____
_____

Saturday: _____
_____
_____
_____

Sunday: _____
_____
_____
_____

Weekly Tracking

Date / Weight	Time	Blood Sugar	Blood Press.	Pulse
Monday				
Weight				
Tuesday				
Weight				
Wednesday				
Weight				
Thursday				
Weight				
Friday				
Weight				
Saturday				
Weight				
Sunday				
Weight				

Weekly Notes

Monday: _____

_____

_____

_____

Tuesday: _____

_____

_____

_____

Wednesday: _____

_____

_____

_____

Thursday: _____

_____

_____

_____

Friday: _____

_____

_____

_____

Saturday: _____

_____

_____

_____

Sunday: _____

_____

_____

_____

Weekly Tracking

Date / Weight	Time	Blood Sugar	Blood Press.	Pulse
Monday				
Weight				
Tuesday				
Weight				
Wednesday				
Weight				
Thursday				
Weight				
Friday				
Weight				
Saturday				
Weight				
Sunday				
Weight				

Weekly Notes

Monday: _____
_____
_____
_____

Tuesday: _____
_____
_____
_____

Wednesday: _____
_____
_____
_____

Thursday: _____
_____
_____
_____

Friday: _____
_____
_____
_____

Saturday: _____
_____
_____
_____

Sunday: _____
_____
_____
_____

Weekly Tracking

Date / Weight	Time	Blood Sugar	Blood Press.	Pulse
Monday				
Weight				
Tuesday				
Weight				
Wednesday				
Weight				
Thursday				
Weight				
Friday				
Weight				
Saturday				
Weight				
Sunday				
Weight				

Weekly Notes

Monday: _____
_____
_____
_____

Tuesday: _____
_____
_____
_____

Wednesday: _____
_____
_____
_____

Thursday: _____
_____
_____
_____

Friday: _____
_____
_____
_____

Saturday: _____
_____
_____
_____

Sunday: _____
_____
_____
_____

Weekly Tracking

Date / Weight	Time	Blood Sugar	Blood Press.	Pulse
Monday				
Weight				
Tuesday				
Weight				
Wednesday				
Weight				
Thursday				
Weight				
Friday				
Weight				
Saturday				
Weight				
Sunday				
Weight				

Weekly Notes

Monday: _____
_____
_____
_____

Tuesday: _____
_____
_____
_____

Wednesday: _____
_____
_____
_____

Thursday: _____
_____
_____
_____

Friday: _____
_____
_____
_____

Saturday: _____
_____
_____
_____

Sunday: _____
_____
_____
_____

Weekly Tracking

Date / Weight	Time	Blood Sugar	Blood Press.	Pulse
Monday				
Weight				
Tuesday				
Weight				
Wednesday				
Weight				
Thursday				
Weight				
Friday				
Weight				
Saturday				
Weight				
Sunday				
Weight				

Weekly Notes

Monday: _____
_____
_____
_____

Tuesday: _____
_____
_____
_____

Wednesday: _____
_____
_____
_____

Thursday: _____
_____
_____
_____

Friday: _____
_____
_____
_____

Saturday: _____
_____
_____
_____

Sunday: _____
_____
_____
_____

Weekly Tracking

Date / Weight	Time	Blood Sugar	Blood Press.	Pulse
Monday				
Weight				
Tuesday				
Weight				
Wednesday				
Weight				
Thursday				
Weight				
Friday				
Weight				
Saturday				
Weight				
Sunday				
Weight				

Weekly Notes

Monday: _____
_____
_____
_____

Tuesday: _____
_____
_____
_____

Wednesday: _____
_____
_____
_____

Thursday: _____
_____
_____
_____

Friday: _____
_____
_____
_____

Saturday: _____
_____
_____
_____

Sunday: _____
_____
_____
_____

Weekly Tracking

Date / Weight	Time	Blood Sugar	Blood Press.	Pulse
Monday				
Weight				
Tuesday				
Weight				
Wednesday				
Weight				
Thursday				
Weight				
Friday				
Weight				
Saturday				
Weight				
Sunday				
Weight				

Weekly Notes

Monday: _____
_____
_____
_____

Tuesday: _____
_____
_____
_____

Wednesday: _____
_____
_____
_____

Thursday: _____
_____
_____
_____

Friday: _____
_____
_____
_____

Saturday: _____
_____
_____
_____

Sunday: _____
_____
_____
_____

Weekly Tracking

Date / Weight	Time	Blood Sugar	Blood Press.	Pulse
Monday				
Weight				
Tuesday				
Weight				
Wednesday				
Weight				
Thursday				
Weight				
Friday				
Weight				
Saturday				
Weight				
Sunday				
Weight				

Weekly Notes

Monday: _____
_____
_____
_____

Tuesday: _____
_____
_____
_____

Wednesday: _____
_____
_____
_____

Thursday: _____
_____
_____
_____

Friday: _____
_____
_____
_____

Saturday: _____
_____
_____
_____

Sunday: _____
_____
_____
_____

Weekly Tracking

Date / Weight	Time	Blood Sugar	Blood Press.	Pulse
Monday				
Weight				
Tuesday				
Weight				
Wednesday				
Weight				
Thursday				
Weight				
Friday				
Weight				
Saturday				
Weight				
Sunday				
Weight				

Weekly Notes

Monday: _____
_____
_____
_____

Tuesday: _____
_____
_____
_____

Wednesday: _____
_____
_____
_____

Thursday: _____
_____
_____
_____

Friday: _____
_____
_____
_____

Saturday: _____
_____
_____
_____

Sunday: _____
_____
_____
_____

Weekly Tracking

Date / Weight	Time	Blood Sugar	Blood Press.	Pulse
Monday				
Weight				
Tuesday				
Weight				
Wednesday				
Weight				
Thursday				
Weight				
Friday				
Weight				
Saturday				
Weight				
Sunday				
Weight				

Weekly Notes

Monday: _____
_____
_____
_____

Tuesday: _____
_____
_____
_____

Wednesday: _____
_____
_____
_____

Thursday: _____
_____
_____
_____

Friday: _____
_____
_____
_____

Saturday: _____
_____
_____
_____

Sunday: _____
_____
_____
_____

Weekly Tracking

Date / Weight	Time	Blood Sugar	Blood Press.	Pulse
Monday				
Weight				
Tuesday				
Weight				
Wednesday				
Weight				
Thursday				
Weight				
Friday				
Weight				
Saturday				
Weight				
Sunday				
Weight				

Weekly Notes

Monday: _____
_____
_____
_____

Tuesday: _____
_____
_____
_____

Wednesday: _____
_____
_____
_____

Thursday: _____
_____
_____
_____

Friday: _____
_____
_____
_____

Saturday: _____
_____
_____
_____

Sunday: _____
_____
_____
_____

Weekly Tracking

Date / Weight	Time	Blood Sugar	Blood Press.	Pulse
Monday				
Weight				
Tuesday				
Weight				
Wednesday				
Weight				
Thursday				
Weight				
Friday				
Weight				
Saturday				
Weight				
Sunday				
Weight				

Weekly Notes

Monday: _____

_____

_____

_____

Tuesday: _____

_____

_____

_____

Wednesday: _____

_____

_____

_____

Thursday: _____

_____

_____

_____

Friday: _____

_____

_____

_____

Saturday: _____

_____

_____

_____

Sunday: _____

_____

_____

_____

Weekly Tracking

Date / Weight	Time	Blood Sugar	Blood Press.	Pulse
Monday				
Weight				
Tuesday				
Weight				
Wednesday				
Weight				
Thursday				
Weight				
Friday				
Weight				
Saturday				
Weight				
Sunday				
Weight				

Weekly Notes

Monday: _____
_____
_____
_____

Tuesday: _____
_____
_____
_____

Wednesday: _____
_____
_____
_____

Thursday: _____
_____
_____
_____

Friday: _____
_____
_____
_____

Saturday: _____
_____
_____
_____

Sunday: _____
_____
_____
_____

Weekly Tracking

Date / Weight	Time	Blood Sugar	Blood Press.	Pulse
Monday				
Weight				
Tuesday				
Weight				
Wednesday				
Weight				
Thursday				
Weight				
Friday				
Weight				
Saturday				
Weight				
Sunday				
Weight				

Weekly Notes

Monday: _____
_____
_____
_____

Tuesday: _____
_____
_____
_____

Wednesday: _____
_____
_____
_____

Thursday: _____
_____
_____
_____

Friday: _____
_____
_____
_____

Saturday: _____
_____
_____
_____

Sunday: _____
_____
_____
_____

Weekly Tracking

Date / Weight	Time	Blood Sugar	Blood Press.	Pulse
Monday				
Weight				
Tuesday				
Weight				
Wednesday				
Weight				
Thursday				
Weight				
Friday				
Weight				
Saturday				
Weight				
Sunday				
Weight				

Weekly Notes

Monday: _____
_____
_____
_____

Tuesday: _____
_____
_____
_____

Wednesday: _____
_____
_____
_____

Thursday: _____
_____
_____
_____

Friday: _____
_____
_____
_____

Saturday: _____
_____
_____
_____

Sunday: _____
_____
_____
_____

Weekly Tracking

Date / Weight	Time	Blood Sugar	Blood Press.	Pulse
Monday				
Weight				
Tuesday				
Weight				
Wednesday				
Weight				
Thursday				
Weight				
Friday				
Weight				
Saturday				
Weight				
Sunday				
Weight				

Weekly Notes

Monday: _____
_____
_____
_____

Tuesday: _____
_____
_____
_____

Wednesday: _____
_____
_____
_____

Thursday: _____
_____
_____
_____

Friday: _____
_____
_____
_____

Saturday: _____
_____
_____
_____

Sunday: _____
_____
_____
_____

Weekly Tracking

Date / Weight	Time	Blood Sugar	Blood Press.	Pulse
Monday				
Weight				
Tuesday				
Weight				
Wednesday				
Weight				
Thursday				
Weight				
Friday				
Weight				
Saturday				
Weight				
Sunday				
Weight				

Weekly Notes

Monday: _____
_____
_____
_____

Tuesday: _____
_____
_____
_____

Wednesday: _____
_____
_____
_____

Thursday: _____
_____
_____
_____

Friday: _____
_____
_____
_____

Saturday: _____
_____
_____
_____

Sunday: _____
_____
_____
_____

Weekly Tracking

Date / Weight	Time	Blood Sugar	Blood Press.	Pulse
Monday				
Weight				
Tuesday				
Weight				
Wednesday				
Weight				
Thursday				
Weight				
Friday				
Weight				
Saturday				
Weight				
Sunday				
Weight				

Weekly Notes

Monday: _____
_____
_____
_____

Tuesday: _____
_____
_____
_____

Wednesday: _____
_____
_____
_____

Thursday:_____
_____
_____
_____

Friday: _____
_____
_____
_____

Saturday: _____
_____
_____
_____

Sunday: _____
_____
_____
_____

Weekly Tracking

Date / Weight	Time	Blood Sugar	Blood Press.	Pulse
Monday				
Weight				
Tuesday				
Weight				
Wednesday				
Weight				
Thursday				
Weight				
Friday				
Weight				
Saturday				
Weight				
Sunday				
Weight				

Weekly Notes

Monday: _____
_____
_____
_____

Tuesday: _____
_____
_____
_____

Wednesday: _____
_____
_____
_____

Thursday: _____
_____
_____
_____

Friday: _____
_____
_____
_____

Saturday: _____
_____
_____
_____

Sunday: _____
_____
_____
_____

Weekly Tracking

Date / Weight	Time	Blood Sugar	Blood Press.	Pulse
Monday				
Weight				
Tuesday				
Weight				
Wednesday				
Weight				
Thursday				
Weight				
Friday				
Weight				
Saturday				
Weight				
Sunday				
Weight				

Weekly Notes

Monday: _____
_____
_____
_____

Tuesday: _____
_____
_____
_____

Wednesday: _____
_____
_____
_____

Thursday: _____
_____
_____
_____

Friday: _____
_____
_____
_____

Saturday: _____
_____
_____
_____

Sunday: _____
_____
_____
_____

Weekly Tracking

Date / Weight	Time	Blood Sugar	Blood Press.	Pulse
Monday				
Weight				
Tuesday				
Weight				
Wednesday				
Weight				
Thursday				
Weight				
Friday				
Weight				
Saturday				
Weight				
Sunday				
Weight				

Weekly Notes

Monday: _____
_____
_____
_____

Tuesday: _____
_____
_____
_____

Wednesday: _____
_____
_____
_____

Thursday: _____
_____
_____
_____

Friday: _____
_____
_____
_____

Saturday: _____
_____
_____
_____

Sunday: _____
_____
_____
_____

Weekly Tracking

Date / Weight	Time	Blood Sugar	Blood Press.	Pulse
Monday				
Weight				
Tuesday				
Weight				
Wednesday				
Weight				
Thursday				
Weight				
Friday				
Weight				
Saturday				
Weight				
Sunday				
Weight				

Weekly Notes

Monday: _____
_____
_____
_____

Tuesday: _____
_____
_____
_____

Wednesday: _____
_____
_____
_____

Thursday: _____
_____
_____
_____

Friday: _____
_____
_____
_____

Saturday: _____
_____
_____
_____

Sunday: _____
_____
_____

Weekly Tracking

Date / Weight	Time	Blood Sugar	Blood Press.	Pulse
Monday				
Weight				
Tuesday				
Weight				
Wednesday				
Weight				
Thursday				
Weight				
Friday				
Weight				
Saturday				
Weight				
Sunday				
Weight				

Weekly Notes

Monday: _____
_____
_____
_____

Tuesday: _____
_____
_____
_____

Wednesday: _____
_____
_____
_____

Thursday:_____
_____
_____
_____

Friday: _____
_____
_____
_____

Saturday: _____
_____
_____
_____

Sunday: _____
_____
_____
_____

Weekly Tracking

Date / Weight	Time	Blood Sugar	Blood Press.	Pulse
Monday				
Weight				
Tuesday				
Weight				
Wednesday				
Weight				
Thursday				
Weight				
Friday				
Weight				
Saturday				
Weight				
Sunday				
Weight				

Weekly Notes

Monday: _____
_____
_____
_____

Tuesday: _____
_____
_____
_____

Wednesday: _____
_____
_____
_____

Thursday: _____
_____
_____
_____

Friday: _____
_____
_____
_____

Saturday: _____
_____
_____
_____

Sunday: _____
_____
_____
_____

Weekly Tracking

Date / Weight	Time	Blood Sugar	Blood Press.	Pulse
Monday				
Weight				
Tuesday				
Weight				
Wednesday				
Weight				
Thursday				
Weight				
Friday				
Weight				
Saturday				
Weight				
Sunday				
Weight				

Weekly Notes

Monday: _____
_____
_____
_____

Tuesday: _____
_____
_____
_____

Wednesday: _____
_____
_____
_____

Thursday: _____
_____
_____
_____

Friday: _____
_____
_____
_____

Saturday: _____
_____
_____
_____

Sunday: _____
_____
_____
_____

Weekly Tracking

Date / Weight	Time	Blood Sugar	Blood Press.	Pulse
Monday				
Weight				
Tuesday				
Weight				
Wednesday				
Weight				
Thursday				
Weight				
Friday				
Weight				
Saturday				
Weight				
Sunday				
Weight				

Weekly Notes

Monday: _____
_____
_____
_____

Tuesday: _____
_____
_____
_____

Wednesday: _____
_____
_____
_____

Thursday: _____
_____
_____
_____

Friday: _____
_____
_____
_____

Saturday: _____
_____
_____
_____

Sunday: _____
_____
_____
_____

Weekly Tracking

Date / Weight	Time	Blood Sugar	Blood Press.	Pulse
Monday				
Weight				
Tuesday				
Weight				
Wednesday				
Weight				
Thursday				
Weight				
Friday				
Weight				
Saturday				
Weight				
Sunday				
Weight				

Weekly Notes

Monday: _____
_____
_____
_____

Tuesday: _____
_____
_____
_____

Wednesday: _____
_____
_____
_____

Thursday: _____
_____
_____
_____

Friday: _____
_____
_____
_____

Saturday: _____
_____
_____
_____

Sunday: _____
_____
_____
_____

Weekly Tracking

Date / Weight	Time	Blood Sugar	Blood Press.	Pulse
Monday				
Weight				
Tuesday				
Weight				
Wednesday				
Weight				
Thursday				
Weight				
Friday				
Weight				
Saturday				
Weight				
Sunday				
Weight				

Weekly Notes

Monday: _____
_____
_____
_____

Tuesday: _____
_____
_____
_____

Wednesday: _____
_____
_____
_____

Thursday: _____
_____
_____
_____

Friday: _____
_____
_____
_____

Saturday: _____
_____
_____
_____

Sunday: _____
_____
_____
_____

Weekly Tracking

Date / Weight	Time	Blood Sugar	Blood Press.	Pulse
Monday				
Weight				
Tuesday				
Weight				
Wednesday				
Weight				
Thursday				
Weight				
Friday				
Weight				
Saturday				
Weight				
Sunday				
Weight				

Weekly Notes

Monday: _____
_____
_____
_____

Tuesday: _____
_____
_____
_____

Wednesday: _____
_____
_____
_____

Thursday: _____
_____
_____
_____

Friday: _____
_____
_____
_____

Saturday: _____
_____
_____
_____

Sunday: _____
_____
_____
_____

Weekly Tracking

Date / Weight	Time	Blood Sugar	Blood Press.	Pulse
Monday				
Weight				
Tuesday				
Weight				
Wednesday				
Weight				
Thursday				
Weight				
Friday				
Weight				
Saturday				
Weight				
Sunday				
Weight				

Weekly Notes

Monday: _____

_____
_____
_____

Tuesday: _____

_____
_____
_____

Wednesday: _____

_____
_____
_____

Thursday: _____

_____
_____
_____

Friday: _____

_____
_____
_____

Saturday: _____

_____
_____
_____

Sunday: _____

_____
_____
_____

Weekly Tracking

Date / Weight	Time	Blood Sugar	Blood Press.	Pulse
Monday				
Weight				
Tuesday				
Weight				
Wednesday				
Weight				
Thursday				
Weight				
Friday				
Weight				
Saturday				
Weight				
Sunday				
Weight				

Weekly Notes

Monday: _____
_____
_____
_____

Tuesday: _____
_____
_____
_____

Wednesday: _____
_____
_____
_____

Thursday:_____
_____
_____
_____

Friday: _____
_____
_____
_____

Saturday: _____
_____
_____
_____

Sunday: _____
_____
_____
_____

Weekly Tracking

Date / Weight	Time	Blood Sugar	Blood Press.	Pulse
Monday				
Weight				
Tuesday				
Weight				
Wednesday				
Weight				
Thursday				
Weight				
Friday				
Weight				
Saturday				
Weight				
Sunday				
Weight				

Weekly Notes

Monday: _____
_____
_____
_____

Tuesday: _____
_____
_____
_____

Wednesday: _____
_____
_____
_____

Thursday: _____
_____
_____
_____

Friday: _____
_____
_____
_____

Saturday: _____
_____
_____
_____

Sunday: _____
_____
_____
_____

Weekly Tracking

Date / Weight	Time	Blood Sugar	Blood Press.	Pulse
Monday				
Weight				
Tuesday				
Weight				
Wednesday				
Weight				
Thursday				
Weight				
Friday				
Weight				
Saturday				
Weight				
Sunday				
Weight				

Weekly Notes

Monday: _____
_____
_____
_____

Tuesday: _____
_____
_____
_____

Wednesday: _____
_____
_____
_____

Thursday: _____
_____
_____
_____

Friday: _____
_____
_____
_____

Saturday: _____
_____
_____
_____

Sunday: _____
_____
_____
_____

Weekly Tracking

Date / Weight	Time	Blood Sugar	Blood Press.	Pulse
Monday				
Weight				
Tuesday				
Weight				
Wednesday				
Weight				
Thursday				
Weight				
Friday				
Weight				
Saturday				
Weight				
Sunday				
Weight				

Weekly Notes

Monday: _____
_____
_____
_____

Tuesday: _____
_____
_____
_____

Wednesday: _____
_____
_____
_____

Thursday: _____
_____
_____
_____

Friday: _____
_____
_____
_____

Saturday: _____
_____
_____
_____

Sunday: _____
_____
_____
_____

Weekly Tracking

Date / Weight	Time	Blood Sugar	Blood Press.	Pulse
Monday				
Weight				
Tuesday				
Weight				
Wednesday				
Weight				
Thursday				
Weight				
Friday				
Weight				
Saturday				
Weight				
Sunday				
Weight				

Weekly Notes

Monday: _____
_____
_____
_____

Tuesday: _____
_____
_____
_____

Wednesday: _____
_____
_____
_____

Thursday: _____
_____
_____
_____

Friday: _____
_____
_____
_____

Saturday: _____
_____
_____
_____

Sunday: _____
_____
_____

Weekly Tracking

Date / Weight	Time	Blood Sugar	Blood Press.	Pulse
Monday				
Weight				
Tuesday				
Weight				
Wednesday				
Weight				
Thursday				
Weight				
Friday				
Weight				
Saturday				
Weight				
Sunday				
Weight				

Weekly Notes

Monday: _____
_____
_____
_____

Tuesday: _____
_____
_____
_____

Wednesday: _____
_____
_____
_____

Thursday: _____
_____
_____
_____

Friday: _____
_____
_____
_____

Saturday: _____
_____
_____
_____

Sunday: _____
_____
_____
_____

Weekly Tracking

Date / Weight	Time	Blood Sugar	Blood Press.	Pulse
Monday				
Weight				
Tuesday				
Weight				
Wednesday				
Weight				
Thursday				
Weight				
Friday				
Weight				
Saturday				
Weight				
Sunday				
Weight				

Weekly Notes

Monday: _____
_____
_____
_____

Tuesday: _____
_____
_____
_____

Wednesday: _____
_____
_____
_____

Thursday: _____
_____
_____
_____

Friday: _____
_____
_____
_____

Saturday: _____
_____
_____
_____

Sunday: _____
_____
_____
_____

Weekly Tracking

Date / Weight	Time	Blood Sugar	Blood Press.	Pulse
Monday				
Weight				
Tuesday				
Weight				
Wednesday				
Weight				
Thursday				
Weight				
Friday				
Weight				
Saturday				
Weight				
Sunday				
Weight				

Weekly Notes

Monday: _____
_____
_____
_____

Tuesday: _____
_____
_____
_____

Wednesday: _____
_____
_____
_____

Thursday: _____
_____
_____
_____

Friday: _____
_____
_____
_____

Saturday: _____
_____
_____
_____

Sunday: _____
_____
_____
_____

Weekly Tracking

Date / Weight	Time	Blood Sugar	Blood Press.	Pulse
Monday				
Weight				
Tuesday				
Weight				
Wednesday				
Weight				
Thursday				
Weight				
Friday				
Weight				
Saturday				
Weight				
Sunday				
Weight				

Weekly Notes

Monday: _____
_____
_____
_____

Tuesday: _____
_____
_____
_____

Wednesday: _____
_____
_____
_____

Thursday: _____
_____
_____
_____

Friday: _____
_____
_____
_____

Saturday: _____
_____
_____
_____

Sunday: _____
_____
_____
_____

Weekly Tracking

Date / Weight	Time	Blood Sugar	Blood Press.	Pulse
Monday				
Weight				
Tuesday				
Weight				
Wednesday				
Weight				
Thursday				
Weight				
Friday				
Weight				
Saturday				
Weight				
Sunday				
Weight				

Weekly Notes

Monday: _____

_____

_____

_____

Tuesday: _____

_____

_____

_____

Wednesday: _____

_____

_____

_____

Thursday: _____

_____

_____

_____

Friday: _____

_____

_____

_____

Saturday: _____

_____

_____

_____

Sunday: _____

_____

_____

_____

Weekly Tracking

Date / Weight	Time	Blood Sugar	Blood Press.	Pulse
Monday				
Weight				
Tuesday				
Weight				
Wednesday				
Weight				
Thursday				
Weight				
Friday				
Weight				
Saturday				
Weight				
Sunday				
Weight				

Weekly Notes

Monday: _____
_____
_____
_____

Tuesday: _____
_____
_____
_____

Wednesday: _____
_____
_____
_____

Thursday: _____
_____
_____
_____

Friday: _____
_____
_____
_____

Saturday: _____
_____
_____
_____

Sunday: _____
_____
_____
_____

Weekly Tracking

Date / Weight	Time	Blood Sugar	Blood Press.	Pulse
Monday				
Weight				
Tuesday				
Weight				
Wednesday				
Weight				
Thursday				
Weight				
Friday				
Weight				
Saturday				
Weight				
Sunday				
Weight				

Weekly Notes

Monday: _____
_____
_____
_____

Tuesday: _____
_____
_____
_____

Wednesday: _____
_____
_____
_____

Thursday: _____
_____
_____
_____

Friday: _____
_____
_____
_____

Saturday: _____
_____
_____
_____

Sunday: _____
_____
_____
_____

Weekly Tracking

Date / Weight	Time	Blood Sugar	Blood Press.	Pulse
Monday				
Weight				
Tuesday				
Weight				
Wednesday				
Weight				
Thursday				
Weight				
Friday				
Weight				
Saturday				
Weight				
Sunday				
Weight				

Weekly Notes

Monday: _____
_____
_____
_____

Tuesday: _____
_____
_____
_____

Wednesday: _____
_____
_____
_____

Thursday: _____
_____
_____
_____

Friday: _____
_____
_____
_____

Saturday: _____
_____
_____
_____

Sunday: _____
_____
_____
_____

Weekly Tracking

Date / Weight	Time	Blood Sugar	Blood Press.	Pulse
Monday				
Weight				
Tuesday				
Weight				
Wednesday				
Weight				
Thursday				
Weight				
Friday				
Weight				
Saturday				
Weight				
Sunday				
Weight				

Weekly Notes

Monday: _____
_____
_____
_____

Tuesday: _____
_____
_____
_____

Wednesday: _____
_____
_____
_____

Thursday: _____
_____
_____
_____

Friday: _____
_____
_____
_____

Saturday: _____
_____
_____
_____

Sunday: _____
_____
_____
_____

Weekly Tracking

Date / Weight	Time	Blood Sugar	Blood Press.	Pulse
Monday				
Weight				
Tuesday				
Weight				
Wednesday				
Weight				
Thursday				
Weight				
Friday				
Weight				
Saturday				
Weight				
Sunday				
Weight				

Weekly Notes

Monday: _____
_____
_____
_____

Tuesday: _____
_____
_____
_____

Wednesday: _____
_____
_____
_____

Thursday: _____
_____
_____
_____

Friday: _____
_____
_____
_____

Saturday: _____
_____
_____
_____

Sunday: _____
_____
_____
_____

Weekly Tracking

Date / Weight	Time	Blood Sugar	Blood Press.	Pulse
Monday				
Weight				
Tuesday				
Weight				
Wednesday				
Weight				
Thursday				
Weight				
Friday				
Weight				
Saturday				
Weight				
Sunday				
Weight				

Weekly Notes

Monday: _____
_____
_____
_____

Tuesday: _____
_____
_____
_____

Wednesday: _____
_____
_____
_____

Thursday: _____
_____
_____
_____

Friday: _____
_____
_____
_____

Saturday: _____
_____
_____
_____

Sunday: _____
_____
_____
_____

Weekly Tracking

Date / Weight	Time	Blood Sugar	Blood Press.	Pulse
Monday				
Weight				
Tuesday				
Weight				
Wednesday				
Weight				
Thursday				
Weight				
Friday				
Weight				
Saturday				
Weight				
Sunday				
Weight				

Weekly Notes

Monday: _____

_____
_____
_____

Tuesday: _____

_____
_____
_____

Wednesday: _____

_____
_____
_____

Thursday: _____

_____
_____
_____

Friday: _____

_____
_____
_____

Saturday: _____

_____
_____
_____

Sunday: _____

_____
_____
_____

Weekly Tracking

Date / Weight	Time	Blood Sugar	Blood Press.	Pulse
Monday				
Weight				
Tuesday				
Weight				
Wednesday				
Weight				
Thursday				
Weight				
Friday				
Weight				
Saturday				
Weight				
Sunday				
Weight				

Weekly Notes

Monday: _____
_____
_____
_____

Tuesday: _____
_____
_____
_____

Wednesday: _____
_____
_____
_____

Thursday: _____
_____
_____
_____

Friday: _____
_____
_____
_____

Saturday: _____
_____
_____
_____

Sunday: _____
_____
_____
_____

Weekly Tracking

Date / Weight	Time	Blood Sugar	Blood Press.	Pulse
Monday				
Weight				
Tuesday				
Weight				
Wednesday				
Weight				
Thursday				
Weight				
Friday				
Weight				
Saturday				
Weight				
Sunday				
Weight				

Weekly Notes

Monday: _____
_____
_____
_____

Tuesday: _____
_____
_____
_____

Wednesday: _____
_____
_____
_____

Thursday: _____
_____
_____
_____

Friday: _____
_____
_____
_____

Saturday: _____
_____
_____
_____

Sunday: _____
_____
_____
_____

Weekly Tracking

Date / Weight	Time	Blood Sugar	Blood Press.	Pulse
Monday				
Weight				
Tuesday				
Weight				
Wednesday				
Weight				
Thursday				
Weight				
Friday				
Weight				
Saturday				
Weight				
Sunday				
Weight				

Notes

Made in United States
North Haven, CT
24 August 2023

40691857R00076